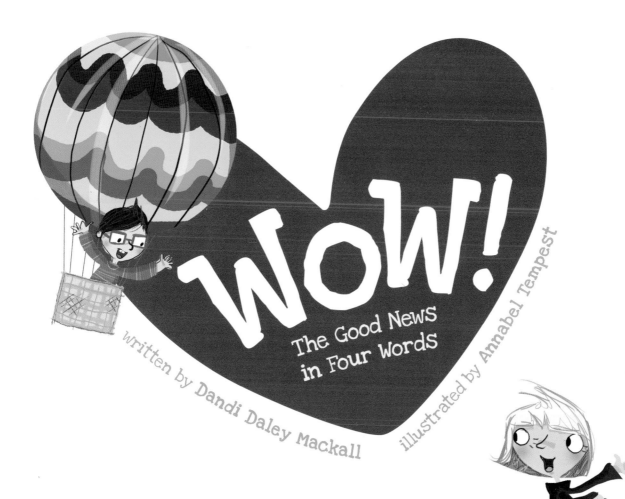

WOW!

The Good News
in Four Words

written by Dandi Daley Mackall

illustrated by Annabel Tempest

10 Publishing
a division of **10** of those.com

D0317245

Originally published in the U.S.A under the title:
Wow! Hardcover, by Dandi Daley Mackall

Copyright © by Dandi Daley Mackall

UK ministry edition © 2017 by 10ofThose Ltd. with permission of Tyndale House Publishers, Inc. All rights reserved.

The concept for this book is based on a sermon by Matt Woodley.

Illustrations by Annabel Tempest. Copyright © Tyndale House Publishers, Inc. All rights reserved.

Edited by Stephanie Rische

Scripture quotations are taken from the Holy Bible, New Living Translation, copyright © 1996, 2004, 2015 by Tyndale House Foundation. Used by permission of Tyndale House Publishers, Inc., Carol Stream, Illinois 60188.
All rights reserved.

Published by 10Publishing, a division of 10ofThose Limited.
ISBN: 978-1-911272-56-4

Designed by: Jacqueline L. Nuñez
Printed in the UK

10Publishing, a division of 10ofthose.com
Unit C, Tomlinson Road, Leyland, Lancashire, PR25 2DY, England

Email: info@10ofthose.com
Website: www.10ofthose.com

For Ellie, Cassie, and Maddie . . .
and all God's children

WOW

Back in the beginning, the world was still dark.

No light and no lightning – not even a spark!

No schools and no houses, no playground or park.

3

Then, **WOW!** All God did was say, "Let there be light!"
He called the light "day", and the dark he called "night".
The world God created was perfect and right.

4

Look up in the sky, because here comes the sun!

At night count the stars, if you can, one by one.

Then gaze at the moon and say, "**WOW**, God! Well done."

5

Just look at the wonders that God had in store,
Like birds, fish, and tigers, and horses and more!
WOW! Creatures with two legs, and creatures with four!

And then God made people – a woman, a man.
For Adam and Eve were both part of God's plan.
They lived in God's Garden. That's where life began.

WOW!

Now Adam and Eve had the world at their feet!
The Garden of Eden held every treat
And only one tree from which no one could eat.

Along came the snake, who was bad as could be.
"Did God say, 'Don't eat'? You should listen to *me*.
That fruit is the best!" And Eve chose to agree.

9

So Eve took a bite. **Uh-oh.** Adam did too.

And God saw it all. "Children, what did you do?"

Since then, we all sin. That means me. That means you.

We have to say, **"Uh-oh."** We're in a bad place.

We can't earn God's favour or talk face-to-face.

We're helpless and hopeless, in need of God's grace.

WOW! **Uh-oh.**

Yes

But God had a wonderful, masterful plan:

"I'll pay for their sin, because only I can.

I'll save the whole world . . . by becoming a man."

12

God loved us so much that he sent us his Son.

So Jesus was born, and the plan was begun.

His life was just perfect. No sin. No, not one.

Yet people grew jealous. "Don't trust him! Beware!"

They had him arrested. His trial was unfair.

He died on a cross. He was crucified there.

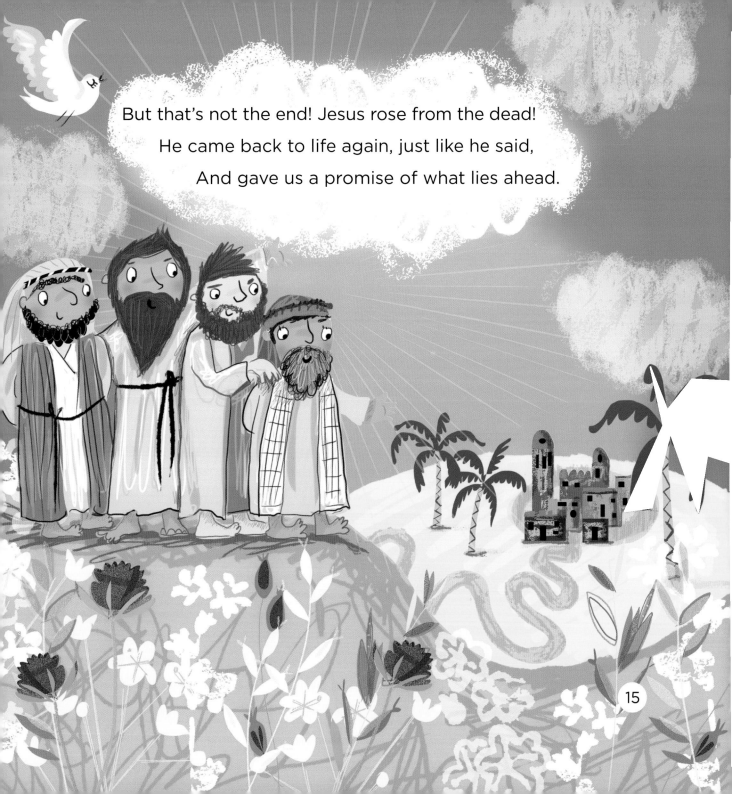

But that's not the end! Jesus rose from the dead!
He came back to life again, just like he said,
And gave us a promise of what lies ahead.

15

For Christ is the Life and the Truth and the Way

For all who believe and receive him today.

Say, "Yes!" and your new life begins right away.

Wow! Uh-oh. Yes!

16

Ahh

Our life is in Jesus, our very best Friend!

He'll always be with us, right up to the end.

For we have the Spirit he promised to send.

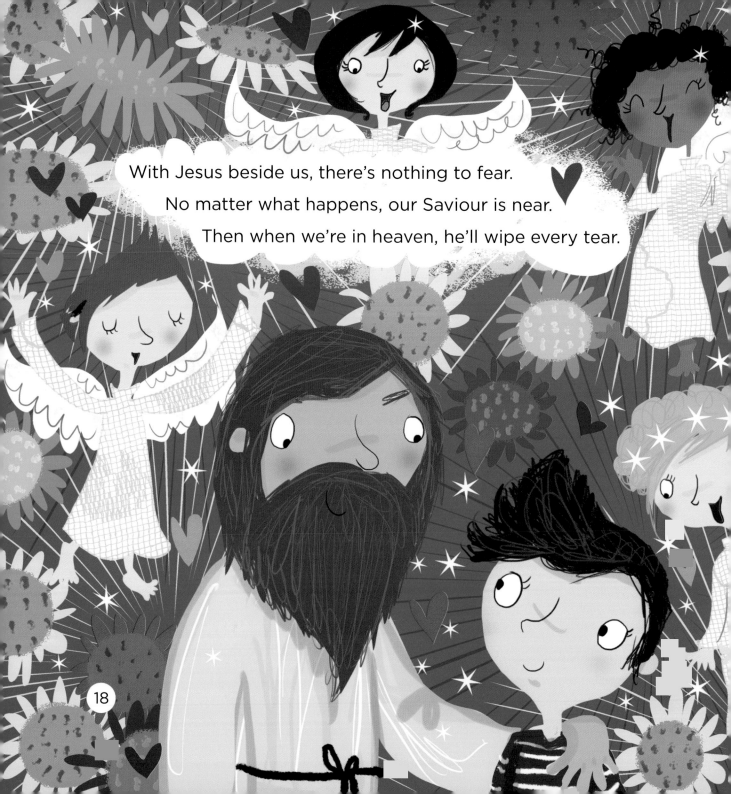

With Jesus beside us, there's nothing to fear.

No matter what happens, our Saviour is near.

Then when we're in heaven, he'll wipe every tear.

We'll join all the angels in heaven to sing,
"All praise to the Father and Jesus the King!
The Ruler of heaven, who made everything!"

19

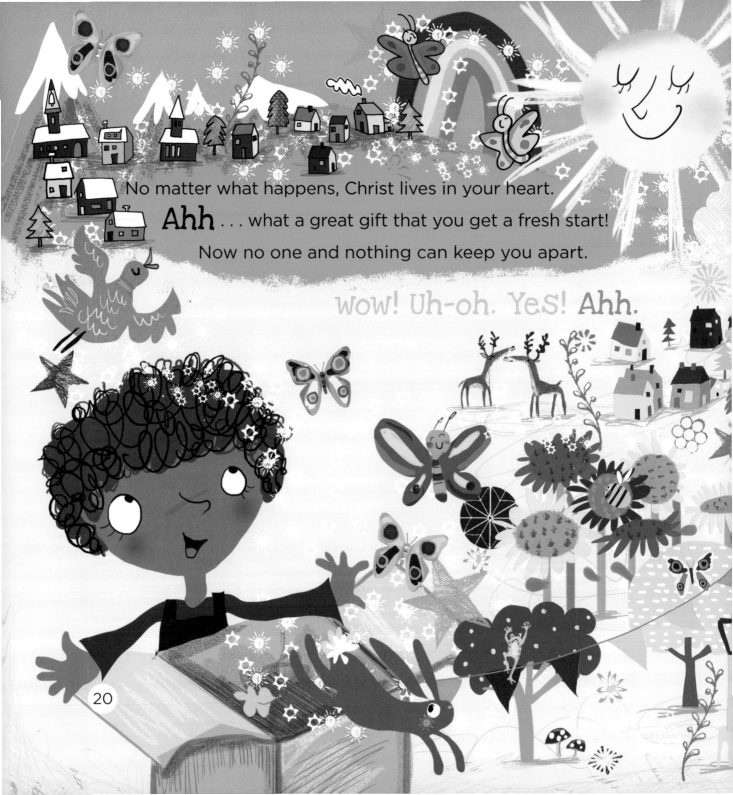

No matter what happens, Christ lives in your heart.

Ahh . . . what a great gift that you get a fresh start!

Now no one and nothing can keep you apart.

Wow! Uh-oh. Yes! Ahh.

WoW

The fruit of the Spirit that's in you will grow.

Now love, joy, and patience are starting to show.

You walk with the Saviour wherever you go.

21

Be thankful for Jesus. Let love overflow.

Tell others God loves them. The world needs to know!

And sharing this news helps your own faith to grow.

23

24

25

For Further Study

Parents, if you want to dig deeper into the gospel with your child (or on your own), here are some Scripture passages that address the ideas in each part. Of course, you can find many more verses throughout the Bible that talk about God's plan for us, but these may give you a place to start.

Genesis 1–2

Psalm 19:1-6

Psalm 24:1-2

Psalm 33:6-9

John 1:1-5

Psalm 25:11

Psalm 41:4

Psalm 51:1-14

Romans 3:12

Romans 3:23-26

Romans 5:19-21

27

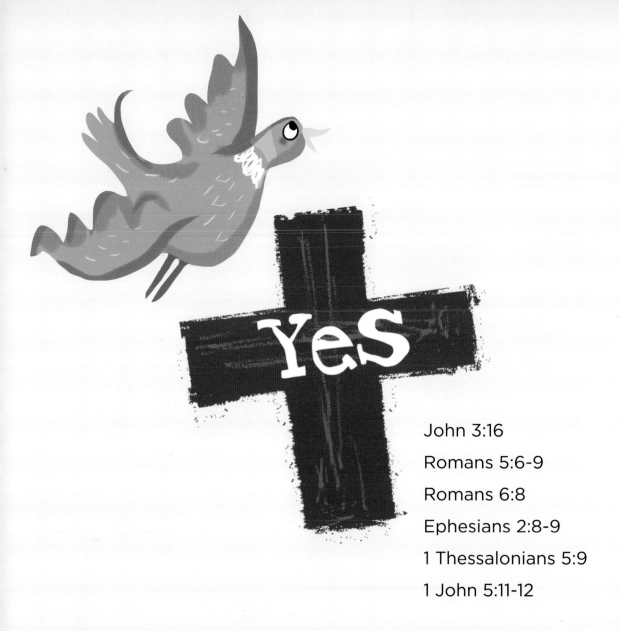

Yes

John 3:16

Romans 5:6-9

Romans 6:8

Ephesians 2:8-9

1 Thessalonians 5:9

1 John 5:11-12

28

Ahh

Psalm 16:5-11

John 14:27

1 Peter 5:7

1 John 5:13-15

Revelation 7:17

Revelation 21:4

WOW

Matthew 28:18-20

Galatians 5:22-23

Colossians 2:7

Colossians 3:16-17

1 John 4:7